Home Voice Studio

A Fast, Easy, Step-by-Step Guide to PC Voice Recording

By Dave Webster

Orange Street Books
Oakland, California

Cover by MadridNYC.com

ISBN: 978-0-615-24217-0
Printed in the USA

Orange Street Books
226 Orange Street
Oakland, CA 94610
info@homevoicestudio.com
www.homevoicestudio.com

Contents

1. Get Up and Running Fast

If you've always wanted to have your own high-quality voice recording studio, but didn't know where to begin, this easy-to-follow guide was written for you. It explains in step-by-step detail everything you need to know to get up and running fast.

You'll find out how to:

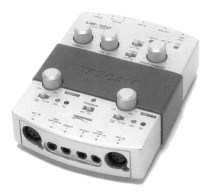

- ► Purchase and install the right equipment
- ► Download and install FREE recording software
- ► Set up your home recording studio
- ► Make professional-quality voice recordings
- ► Edit your recordings
- ► Save your recordings as Wave files, MP3s, and more
- ► Add music and sound effects to your recordings

The major hurdle for home recording has always been figuring out how to do it. Not anymore. Now all you need to make studio-quality voice recordings at home is 1) your desktop or laptop PC, 2) FREE recording software that we'll show you how to get, and 3) audio equipment that you can purchase for just a few hundred dollars. In this guide, you'll find out exactly what you need, where to get it, and how to use it.

With this step-by-step guide, you'll be up and running with your home voice studio in no time. Our goal is not to turn you into a recording engineer, but simply to show you how to start making high-quality voice recordings as quickly and easily as possible.

Everything you need to know in less than 30 pages

Most how-to books make you wade through page-after-page of time-wasting filler. Not this one. *Home Voice Studio* is short on filler, and it's packed with everything you need to know to get started fast.

Perfect for voiceover

The good news for voiceover actors is that there's more work available now than ever before. Voiceover used to be restricted to TV, radio, and corporate videos. Now we have computer games, podcasting, Flash demos, Web audio, e-Books, e-Learning programs, voicemail messaging—the list goes on and on—and they all need voice talent.

Inexpensive, high-quality home recording is the best thing that's ever happened to voiceover actors. Most agents don't even bother calling their actors in for auditions anymore—they just email us the scripts and let us record our own auditions and email them in. There's also a growing number of voice casting websites, for which high-quality home recording capability is a must. And if you're just getting started in voiceover, there's no better way to practice than having your own home studio.

Do paid voiceover gigs from home

Besides auditions and practice, you can use your home studio for a wide variety of non-commercial voiceover jobs—including Flash and video narrations, e-learning programs, Web audio, voicemail messaging, and more—all you have to do is record the client's script and email them the audio files. You can make money doing voiceovers without even leaving the house!

Great for coaches, trainers, teachers, and therapists, too

You don't have to be a voice actor to benefit from high-quality home recording. Professional therapists, coaches, teachers, trainers, and others are building lucrative income streams by recording and selling their own CDs. A home voice studio is perfect for all of these uses and more. You can even add music to your recordings (see chapter 7).

How much does it cost?

Using your desktop or laptop Windows PC, free downloadable recording software, and audio equipment that costs as little as $200 (see chapter 2), you'll get quality that's practically indistinguishable from what you'd expect from a professional recording studio.

Get up and running quickly

Just follow the step-by-step instructions in this guide, and once you get your equipment, you'll be making professional quality recordings in a matter of hours. We'll show you what hardware you need and where to get it, how to download FREE, easy-to-use recording software, how to set up your home studio, how to record and edit high quality voice files and save them as Wave or MP3 files, and even how to add music and sound effects.

About the author

Dave Webster is a *CLIO*, *Addy*, and *Silver Microphone* award-winning voiceover actor with more than ten years of experience in commercials, corporate and industrial projects, video games, Web audio, podcasting, e-learning programs, and more. A few years ago, agents started asking him to record his own audition files from home, so he went out and bought a mic and a USB audio interface. Since he had no idea how to hook up and use this stuff, it ended up collecting dust for several months while he continued to pay through the nose for studio fees every time he needed to record something.

Dave finally paid a sound engineer a couple hundred dollars to show him how to hook up his equipment and use it. Now you can get the benefits of what he learned, and for a small fraction of what he had to pay. But enough about him ... let's get started!

2. Choosing the Right Hardware

Shopping list:
- ❑ Condenser microphone
- ❑ Mic stand, mic cable, pop filter
- ❑ USB audio interface with built-in pre-amp
- ❑ Good-quality powered speakers and over-the-ear headphones (recommended)
- ❑ Music stand (recommended)

You only need a few pieces of basic equipment for your home studio, all of which you can purchase from any good musical equipment retailer. Check your yellow pages or do an online search for "musical instruments dealers" or "professional audio equipment."

Ordering online is easy, although visiting a music store in person gives you the benefit of talking to a knowledgeable sales person who can answer your questions and give you advice on what to buy. Tell them you want to use your computer to record your speaking voice and that you need a **condenser microphone**; **a mic stand**, **mic cable**, and **pop filter**; a **USB audio interface with built-in pre-amp**; and a music stand (optional). They'll also have good quality powered speakers and headphones available (optional).

Condenser mic* – $200 and up

The mic is your most important piece of equipment. If you use a low quality mic, your voice is not going to sound good, so spend enough to get a decent one. I use an Audio-Technica AT3035, which retails for around $200. The Rode NT1-A is also an excellent choice for a reasonably priced high-quality mic (around $230), and there are other good choices available. Talk to your music store sales person for other recommendations. If you're on a tight budget, look into the Audio-Technica AT2020, which retails for around $100 and delivers excellent results.

*Microphone types – The two main types of microphone are "dynamic" and "condenser." Dynamic mics are less expensive and more rugged than condenser mics, but they're not sensitive enough for high-quality voiceover work. A condenser mic will pick up all the subtle nuances of your vocal delivery. The mics discussed above are condenser mics. **Avoid USB Mics**. They use your computer's sound card to process the signal, which produces inferior sound quality compared to an external USB audio interface (discussed on the next page).

Microphone accessories

1. <u>Mic stand</u> – **$10-15** for a basic stand like the one pictured here →
2. <u>Shockmount</u> – **$25 and up**. The shockmount isolates the mic from vibrations. Many mics come with a shockmount, including the ones discussed above.
3. <u>Mic cable</u> – **$10-20**.
4. <u>Pop filter</u> – **$15 and up**. A pop filter (pictured at right) cuts down on the breathy "plosive" sounds that the mic picks up from P's and B's. Not absolutely necessary, but recommended.
5. <u>Music stand</u> – **$10 and up**. Not essential, but you'll need something to hold your copy.

USB audio interface – $100 and up

The USB audio interface processes the signal from the mic and sends it to your computer. It also provides power to your condenser mic and lets you adjust mic input levels. I use a Tascam US-122 (pictured), and there are other quality brands available, including M-Audio and Digidesign.

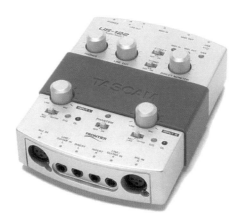

Speakers and headphones

High-quality speakers are much more accurate than the ones that come with most computers. Powered speakers ($100 and up) can be plugged into your computer's speaker or headphone jacks. Headphones ($50 and up) are also very useful for critical listening.

Connecting your hardware to your PC

Step 1: Make sure your PC or laptop has the minimum required processor and memory. The information that comes with your USB audio interface will tell you what's needed. If your computer is no more than a few years old, you should have no trouble. If you're using an older computer, you might have problems, so consider replacing it with a newer one.

Step 2: Install your USB audio interface: Read the installation instructions that came with your USB interface and follow them carefully. In most cases, all you need to do is load the software and then connect the interface to one of your computer's USB ports. If you have any trouble, don't hesitate to call the company's tech-support phone number.

Step 3: Choose your USB interface as your "default recording device": For Windows XP, click "**start**" at the lower left corner of your screen, then click "**Control Panel.**"

NOTE for Windows VISTA users: The images in this guide are for Windows XP. For Windows Vista, all you have to do is load the USB interface software and then plug the interface into a USB port on your computer.

Step 4: Click "**Sounds, Speech, and Audio Devices**."

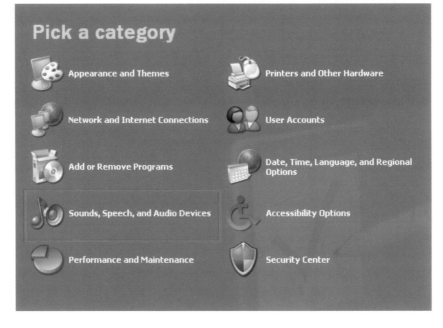

Step 5: Click "**Sounds and Audio Devices**."

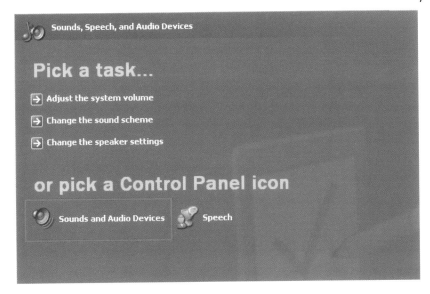

Step 6 : Click the "**Audio**" tab →

Step 7: Choose your USB audio interface from the "**Sound recording**" drop-down menu.

Step 8: Click "**OK**."

Step 9: Close the control panel by clicking the red "**X**" in the upper right corner.

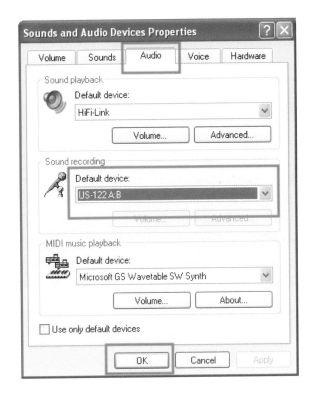

(NOTE: If you have trouble installing your USB audio interface, or if the setup instructions are unclear (a common situation, unfortunately), call the company's tech support line for help. There should be a phone number in the product info or on the company's website. If they can't or won't help you, return the equipment and buy a different brand!)

3. Free Recording Software

Now that you have your equipment set up, all you have to do is install recording software onto your computer. I recommend a program called **WavePad**, made by an Australian company called **NCH Swift Sound**. It's very easy to use, and it's perfect for recording one or two voices.

You can use WavePad to record and edit your voice files, remove unwanted noises, apply special effects, save your recordings as MP3 and Wave files, and more. You can **download WavePad FREE** at http://www.nch.com.au/wavepad/index.html.

You can also purchase **WavePad Master's Edition**, which includes a few additional features, for around $50. NCH Swift Sound also has dozens of other useful sound recording and telephony programs you might want to check out.

WavePad audio recording and editing software

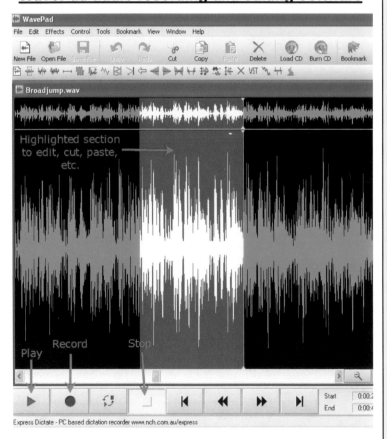

*From http://www.nch.com.au/wavepad/index.html

About WavePad*

"This audio editing software is a full featured professional sound editor for Windows or Mac. It lets you make and edit music, voice, and other audio recordings. When editing audio files, you can cut, copy, and paste parts of recordings and, if required, add effects like echo, amplification and noise reduction. WavePad works as a wav editor or mp3 editor but it also supports a number of other file formats including vox, gsm, real audio, au, aif, flac, ogg, and more.

WavePad is designed to be very easy and intuitive to use for audio editing. Within minutes you will be able to open or record a file and edit it. But if you take time to explore the other features, you will find many powerful tools for editing audio designed with the professional sound engineer in mind...."

Other recording software

There are other excellent voice recording programs available, costing from less than $100 to several hundred dollars. However, given WavePad's ease of use and the fact that you can download it for free, I recommend at least starting with it. If you need more advanced features later on, you can always upgrade after you've mastered the basics. I've been home recording for a few years now, and I've been able to do everything I need to do with WavePad.

Downloading and installing WavePad

Step 1: Go to http://www.nch.com.au/wavepad/index.html

You'll see the screen pictured here. Click "**Download WavePad**."

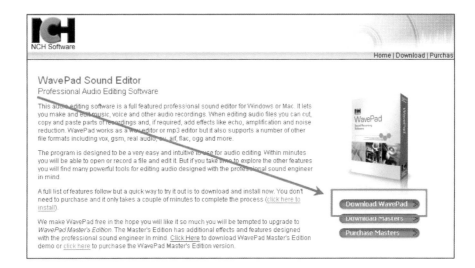

Step 2: Click "**Save File**."

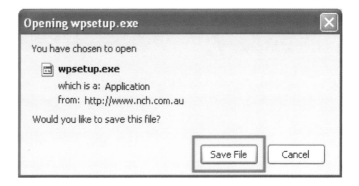

(NOTE: If you have trouble downloading or installing WavePad, go to NCH Swift Sound's support page: http://www.nch.com.au/support/index.html.)

Step 3: After WavePad finishes downloading to your computer, click "**Open**" in the Downloads window, or ...

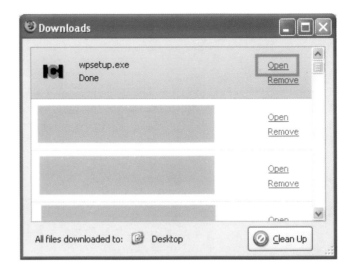

... double click the "**wpsetup**" icon on your desktop.

Step 4: If your computer asks, "**Open Executable file?**" click "**OK**."

Step 5: "**License Agreement**" – Click "**I agree with these terms**," then click "**next**."

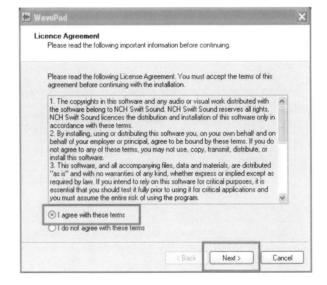

Step 6: Click "**Finish**" to complete the installation.

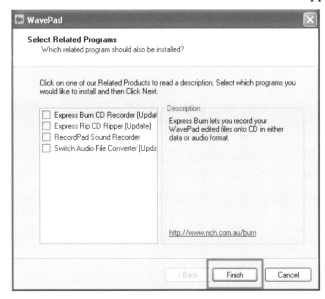

Step 7: Check to make sure that WavePad is installed by looking for the **WavePad** shortcut icon on your desktop. Double click it to open the program. If you don't see the shortcut, just click _start_ , then "**All Programs**," and then click "**WavePad**" on your program list.

Step 8: Here's what you'll see when WavePad opens (the Windows Vista version has a slightly different look, but all the controls are the same).

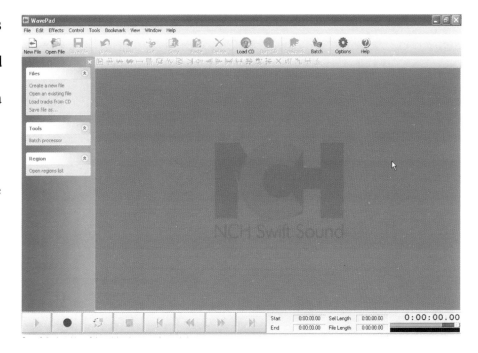

4. Setting up Your Home Studio

Find a quiet place to record

It's important to find a quiet place to record. Anything *you* can hear when you're standing in front of the mic—car horns, sirens, barking dogs, screaming kids, home appliances, TVs, air conditioners, and even the cooling fan in your computer—will also be audible in your recordings, so find a place where you can minimize these background noises.

Walk-in closets are ideal for home recording. They usually don't have windows, which means less noise coming in from outside. Plus, all the clothes cut down on reflected sounds. You can also put a small rug or piece of carpet on the floor to further reduce reflections and hang blankets or foam on the walls and doors.

Having your computer in front of you while you're recording is convenient, but it's not essential. You can always put the computer in another room and run a long mic cable. If you plan to record right next to your computer, you'll need to block the noise from the computer's cooling fan by either placing the computer inside a soundproof enclosure or using a recording booth or Porta-Booth (see next page). Some laptops are quiet enough to use inside your recording room, but many are not.

Setting up your microphone

Step 1: Attach your microphone shockmount to the mic stand by screwing it onto the threaded fitting.

Step 2: Place your mic in the shockmount, and plug in your mic cable.

Step 3: Plug the other end of the cable into your USB audio interface (either L or R channel is fine).

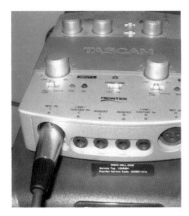

Step 4: Turn on the interface's "**phantom power**" switch (powers the mic). If your interface has a switch with settings for "mic" and "guitar," set it to "mic."

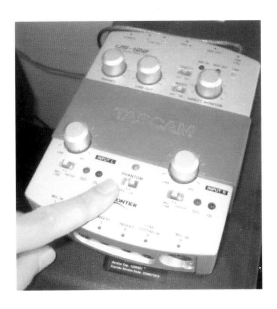

Sound Booths

If you have extra money and floor space, you can buy a high-quality vocal booth or "whisper room" as they're sometimes called. Just do a Web search for "vocal booths." If you're handy, you can build your own booth. Many of the places that sell booths and recording equipment also sell acoustic insulation foam and other materials.

Don't have space or money for a booth? The Porta-Booth → isolates just the mic instead of both the mic and you. It's just big enough for a mic on a tabletop stand. Great if you need to record when you're away from home. Costs around $130. You can buy it on Amazon.com.

5. Making Professional Recordings

While you're getting started, it's a good idea to place the mic next to your computer so you can watch what happens on the monitor as you're recording. Once you know what you're doing, you can move the mic to a quieter spot to eliminate background noises.

Step 1: Open WavePad by double clicking the WavePad icon on your desktop, or by clicking "**Start**," "**All Programs**," "**WavePad**."

Step 2: After WavePad opens, click the "**New File**" icon or press "**Ctrl-N**" to create a new file.

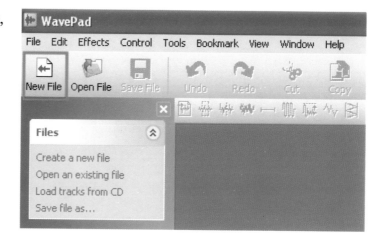

NOTE: For most WavePad commands, you can either mouse click icons and dropdown lists or use keyboard commands. I'll be referring to both in these instructions.

Step 3: WavePad will prompt you to choose a "**Sample Rate**." The sample rate determines the quality of your recording. Choose 44100 (CD quality) or above. Click "**Mono**" if you're recording from just one microphone, or "**Stereo**" if you want to use two mics and keep the voices on separate channels. Then click "**OK**."

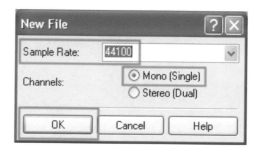

You'll see a blank window, like this →

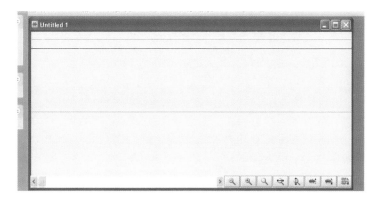

Step 4: Click the red **Record** button on the lower left corner of your screen or press **F5**.

Step 5: The **Record Control** window will appear on your screen. Make sure the **Recording Device** selected is your USB interface, and that the **Input** mode selected is "**Wave**." If not, select them from the drop-down lists, then close and reopen WavePad and go back to **Step 2**.

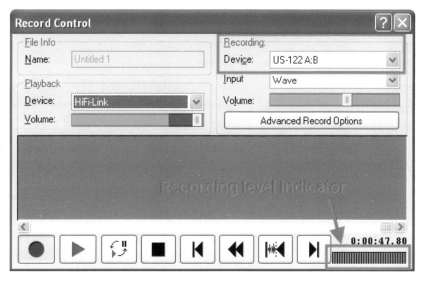

Speak into the mic, making sure the recording level indicator in the lower right corner of the window does not go all the way to the maximum (red lines go all the way to the right) and stay there, or your recording will be distorted. To adjust the recording level, use the "mic" or "line" input volume knob on your USB interface. You can also try standing farther from the mic (6 – 8" is usually good). With a little practice, you'll get a feel for where to stand and how to adjust the input level.

Stand about 6-8 inches from the mic. With condenser mics, you speak into the side of the mic, not the end. The photo here (shown without a pop filter) is the view you should have of your condenser mic when it's positioned correctly.

To help reduce "plosives"—bursts of air produced by "P" sounds—it's a good idea to use a pop filter. You can also experiment with mic placement. Placing the mic a little bit "off axis" (slightly to the side instead of straight in front of your mouth) keeps the plosives from hitting the mic head-on.

Step 6: When you're finished with your take, close the window by clicking the "**X**" at the upper right corner of the **Record Control** window, or by pressing the **Esc** key at the upper left corner of your keyboard.

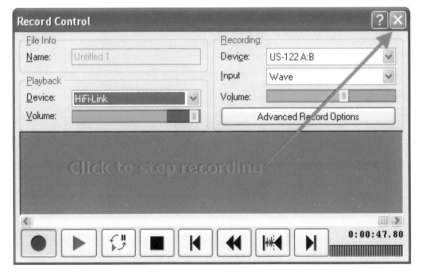

When the Record Control window closes, you'll see a waveform (jagged vertical lines) on your screen.

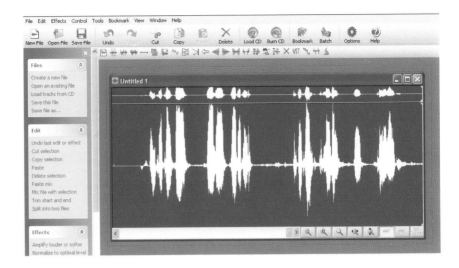

To listen to your recording, click the green "**play**" button or press **F9**.

To stop, click "**stop**" (black square) or press the **Esc** key.

Troubleshooting: "I don't see or hear anything"

Step 1: Make sure the microphone cord is plugged into both the mic and the USB interface. Make sure the USB interface cord is plugged into both the interface and the computer. Make sure the volume on your speakers is turned up loud enough to hear.

Step 2: Make sure your USB interface's "Phantom Power" switch is turned on, and that the "mic / guitar" switch (if it has one) is set to "mic."

Step 3: Press **F5** to open the **Record Control** window and make sure the **Recording Device** selected is your USB interface and that **Input** mode is "**Wave**." If not, select them from the drop-down lists.

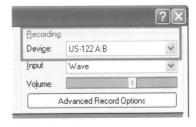

Step 4: Click "**Advanced Record Options**." The "**Advanced Settings**" window will open. Make sure "**Auto Start Recording**" is checked.

Step 5: Close WavePad, then start again with **Step 1** at the top of page 14. If you're still having problems, call the tech support number for your USB interface for help.

Always make a backup file

After you've finished recording, always back up your work before you do any editing in case you make a mistake and have to start the editing process over.

Step 1: Click "**File**," "**Save file**," or press **Ctrl-S**. In the "**Save as type**" line → choose "**Wave (.wav)**."

Name the file "**[project name] backup**" so you can find it easily, then click "**Save**."

Step 2: The box pictured to the right will appear. For **Format**, choose "**PCM**." For "**Attributes**" choose **44.100 kHz, 16 Bit Mono**" (or **16 Bit, Stereo** if you're recording with two mics and want it to be in stereo).

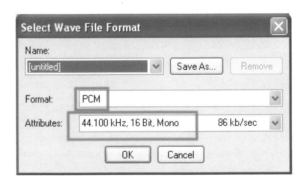

"PCM" is a type of formatting that doesn't alter the sound in any way; you can save and reopen the file as many times as you want with no loss in quality. "MP3" and other formats "compress" the digital audio information, degrading the sound quality a little bit each time you save the file.

If you're going to do any editing, save your file again right away under a different name. This way, you won't accidentally save your work over your original backup file. Click "**File**," "**Save File As**," type in a different name, then click "**Save**," then "**OK**."

6. Editing Your Recordings

Let's say you get a decent take, but you're not happy with one or two sentences. No problem—WavePad makes it easy to redo just that one section. You can start your retake anywhere, as long as there's a clean break between words.

Don't forget to make a **backup file** in case you need to start over (see previous page: "**Make a Backup file**").

Step 1: "Maximize" the waveform window so it'll be easier to see and work with, by clicking the small box icon at the upper right corner of the window.

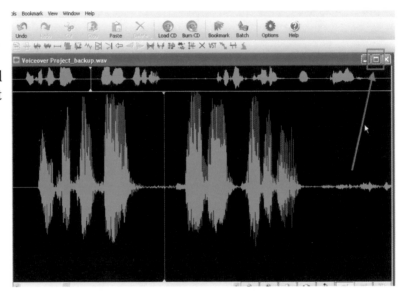

Click the "zoom in" icon (magnifying glass with +) or press "**Ctrl +** " to "stretch out" the waveform and make it easier to pinpoint specific areas in your waveform. Click "zoom out" (magnifying glass with -) or press "**Ctrl -** " to squeeze it back down when you want to view larger sections of the waveform.

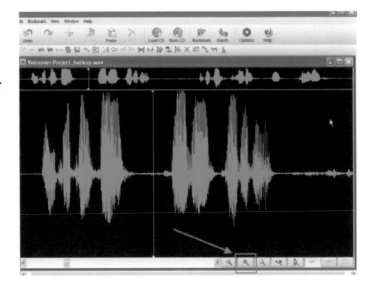

Step 2: If you want to re-record a section, highlight that section by placing the cursor at the beginning of the section, and then clicking and dragging the cursor to the end point. The section will be highlighted in blue. Confirm that it's the right section by clicking the green "**play**" button or pressing **F9** to listen, so you don't accidentally re-record the wrong section. If you make a mistake, just click "**Edit**," "**Undo**."

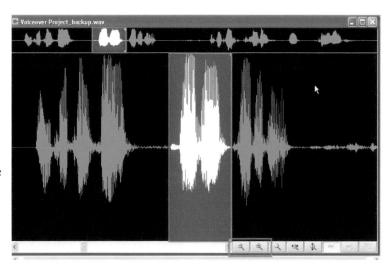

Step 3: Click the red "**record**" button or press **F5** and then re-record. When you're finished, click the "**X**" to close the **Record Control** window or press the **Esc** key. The new waveform will appear where the original highlighted section was. The length of the re-recorded section does not have to match the length of the original section—WavePad will adjust automatically.

Removing breaths and noises

Removing noisy breaths and other unwanted sounds in your recordings is easy. Just highlight the section of the waveform you want to cut by clicking and dragging the cursor, then click "**Edit**," "**Cut**" or press **Ctrl-X**. The small "lump" in the waveform pictured at right is what a typical breath looks like.

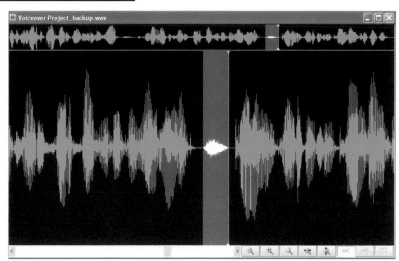

NOTE: Keep in mind that some audible breaths in a recording are normal. When you have to take a deep breath, you can turn your head slightly so the mic doesn't pick up the full volume. If it's too loud, you can cut it out completely, or use noise reduction, explained on the next page and in WavePad's Help menu (click **Help**, **Help Contents**, **Effects**, **Noise Reduction**).

Removing breaths and noises (cont.)

If you want to remove a breath or other noise, but need to maintain a pause of a certain length (between sentences for example) you can do one of two things:

1. Highlight the relevant section of your waveform, and then <u>click the noise reduction icon</u> in the toolbar. The Noise Reduction window will appear. Setting the "**Noise Gate Level**" to 0 dB will replace any sound in the section you've highlighted with total silence.

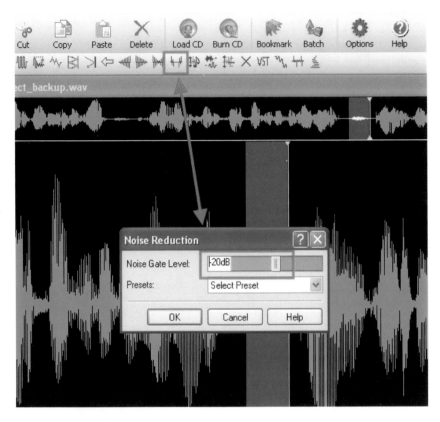

If you accidentally erase something you want to keep, just click the "**undo**" icon or press **Ctrl-Z**.

2. **The other way to get rid of noise** is to copy a "quiet section" of the desired length (below left); copy by clicking **Edit, Copy** or pressing **Ctrl-C**; then highlight the unwanted noise (below right) and paste in the quiet section (click **Edit, Paste** or press **Ctrl-V**).

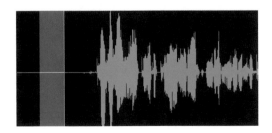

Improving the quality of your recordings

After you've recorded and edited your file and you're happy with how it sounds, you can further improve the sound quality with special tools included in WavePad. It's a little complicated for this beginner's guide, but if you're interested, I recommend spending some time exploring WavePad's excellent help screens: click **Help**, **Help Contents**, **Effects**, **Noise Reduction**.

Reducing volume spikes

If you have sections that are noticeably louder than the rest of your take, it's easy to make adjustments. To reduce a too-loud section, like the one pictured at right (noticeably bigger waveform), highlight that section, then click "**Effects**," "**Normalize**." The Normalize window will appear →

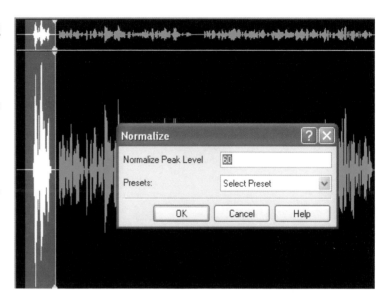

Type in a number between 1 and 100 (try 90 first, then 80, and so on), then click "**OK**." Click "**undo**" if it doesn't sound right and then try again. Try various settings until 1) the height of the waveform matches the rest of your recording and 2) the volume is even.

Amplifying volume

To amplify sections that aren't loud enough, highlight the section that needs a volume boost, then click "**Effects**," "**Amplify**." The Amplify window will appear. Try different settings (120, 150, etc.) until it looks and sounds right, clicking "**undo**" to go back and try again.

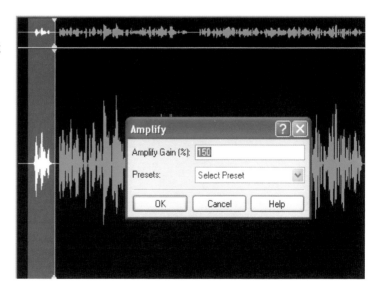

Maximizing volume

After you've done all
your editing and noise
reduction, you can get
better overall sound
quality by maximizing
the volume of your entire
recording. Use the
Normalize command
again. First, select the
entire waveform by
pressing **Ctrl-A**, then
click "**Effects**,"

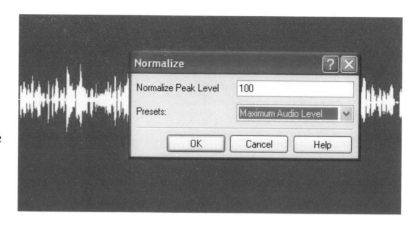

"**Normalize**." Type "**100**" in the "**Normalize Peak Level**" window, or choose
"**Maximum Audio Level**" (does the same thing), then click "**OK**." Your waveform will
expand vertically and you'll get a fuller sound.

Saving your recording

After you're done recording and editing, you can save your work in Wave or MP3
formats, or any of the several other file formats supported by WavePad.

Step 1: Click
"**File**," "**Save File
As**."

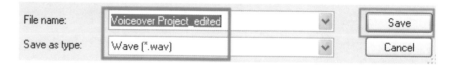

Type in a name for your file, choose "**Wave**" from the **Save as type** drop-down list, then
click "**Save**."

Step 2: You'll be prompted to choose a
Format for your file. Different file formats
have different settings. Always save your
files first as **Wave, PCM, 44.100 kHz, 16-
bit mono**, in case you need to do more
editing later. Click "**OK**." Then click
"**File**," "**Save File As**" and save the file
again under a different name.

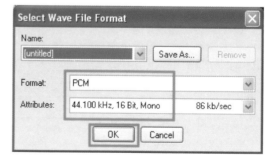

If you're recording for your agent or a client, ask what "file specs" they want (example:
"MP3 with 128 kbps bitrate"). Click "**File**," "**Save File As**," and save the file using those
specs. For auditions and many industrial projects, it'll usually be **MP3** or **Wave PCM**.

7. Adding Music to Your Recordings

If you want to mix music with your voice file,* follow the steps in this section. It's a little tricky at first, and it'll probably take you a few tries before you get your mix just the way you want it, so treat it as a learning experience. And be sure to save a backup file before you start mixing!

Step 1: Open the voice file you want to add music to.

Step 2: Choose where you want the music to begin. Click the waveform at that spot.

Step 3: Click "**Edit**" from the top menu bar, then "**Mix File**" from the drop-down list.

Step 4: Select the music file you want to use.

Step 5: Click "**Open.**"

Step 6: You'll be prompted to enter a "**Mix Volume (%)**." Type in a number between "**1**" and "**100**," depending on how loud you want the music relative to the voice: "**100**" will mix the music at the same volume as in its original file, "**50**" will be half as loud, and so on. Click "**OK**" to mix the files. Try various levels until you get it right, clicking "**undo**" to go back and start over.

*DON'T GET SUED! If your client wants music mixed in with your voice, ask them to provide the music file and emphasize that any copyright issues, licensing payments, and so on are their sole responsibility.

8. Additional Resources

At this point, you have everything you need to start making your own studio-quality voice recordings. When you're ready to learn more, the WavePad help menu is an excellent place to start (click "**Help**," "**Help Contents**" or press **F1**). You can search for specific topics, or just browse the various areas to learn more about the digital recording process.

Learn more about digital recording

If you want to learn more about digital audio recording, Lynda.com has some excellent online courses. Go to http://movielibrary.lynda.com/html/modPage.asp?ID=338 to view free sample lessons. There are also many books available on advanced recording techniques. Check Amazon.com. You can also find courses on audio engineering by doing a Web search for "audio engineering courses, [your city]."

Made in the USA
Lexington, KY
18 December 2011